Back to Basics

ENGLISH

for 8–9 year olds

BOOK TWO

Sheila Lane and Marion Kemp

The alphabet

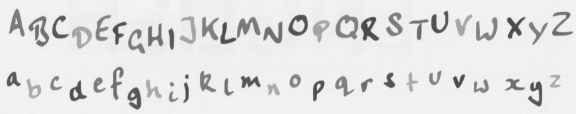

What's next?
Write the next letter in the series.

e f g ☐   a b c ☐   o p q ☐

U V W X Y ☐   F G H I J ☐   Q R S T U ☐

Write the missing letters.   k ☐ m n ☐ p q r ☐ t u v ☐

G H I ☐ K L M ☐ O P Q ☐ S T U ☐

A B ☐ d e ☐ G H ☐ j k l ☐

Write each set of nouns in **alphabetical order**.

fish ☐   Wales ☐   tribe ☐

insect ☐   Scotland ☐   pack ☐

bird ☐   Ireland ☐   bunch ☐

reptile ☐   England ☐   fleet ☐

Write each set of verbs in **alphabetical order**.

yell ☐   talk ☐   skip ☐

cry ☐   smile ☐   trot ☐

shout ☐   laugh ☐   run ☐

roar ☐   chat ☐   jog ☐

When more than one word in a set begins with the **same** letter, you need to look at the **second** letter of the word.

bang
bite
busy

Write the missing first letters for the pictures.

[ ] orch   [ ] able   [ ] iger   [ ] elescope

[ ] ird   [ ] ook   [ ] us   [ ] all

Write the complete words in **alphabetical order**.

Arrange the words in the box in **alphabetical order**.

| single |
| sure |
| several |
| same |
| solid |

| boast |
| beyond |
| bitter |
| burn |
| bare |

Look up the meaning of each word in your dictionary and write it here.

Grammar

A **noun** is a naming word.

An **adjective** is a word which describes a noun.

an apple

a juicy apple

Which adjectives best describe the nouns? Join them up.

1   a soft   knife
2   a sharp   mountain
3   an empty   monster
4   a high   cup
5   an ugly   cushion

6   a round   sea
7   a tasty   soldier
8   a stormy   face
9   a brave   sausage
10 a happy   circle

Write an **adjective** of your own choice to describe each noun.

1   a [   ] wall
2   a [   ] pencil
3   a [   ] dinner

4   a [   ] pillow
5   a [   ] ring
6   an [   ] bucket

Write a **noun** of your own choice for each adjective.

1   an enormous [   ]
2   a sweet [   ]
3   a heavy [   ]

4   a fluffy [   ]
5   a bright [   ]
6   a dark [   ]

Write this sentence in your best handwriting:

An adjective describes a noun.

....

....

4

yellow bananas
gold corn

silver paper
white snow

The names
of colours are
adjectives.

Write a **colour** adjective in each space.

1   a field of [   ] grass   4   the [   ] sky

2   the [   ] sun   5   [   ] coins

3   a [   ] holly berry   6   a [   ] light

There are two kinds of number adjectives:

number words . . . two   **order of place** . . . second
                     ten   tenth

Join the **number word** to the **order number** that matches it.

1   one   fourth   4   nine   twelfth

2   four   sixth   5   eleven   ninth

3   six   first   6   twelve   eleventh

Write an **adjective** in each space.

1   The Union Jack is [   ] , [   ] and [   ] .

2   The [   ] letter of the alphabet is C.

3   January is the [   ] month of the year.

4   I have [   ] toes on each foot.

5   The Christmas tree had [   ] and [   ] decorations.

Spelling

I slid down a slide.

'**Silent e**' makes the short vowel in the middle of a word have a long sound.

Say . . . f<u>i</u>n
and f<u>i</u>ne

Say . . . h<u>o</u>p
and h<u>o</u>pe

Cross off the letter **e** at the end of each word.
Draw a picture of the new word in the box.

hate `hat`

care

pine

mate

cape

pane

1	2	3	4	5
LOOK	**SAY**	**COVER**	**WRITE**	**CHECK**

This is a way to learn to spell correctly.

When you know the words in the box, cover them with a small piece of paper.
Write the words by the pictures.

Check your spelling with ✔ or ✗

tape
kite
note
pipe
cube
tube

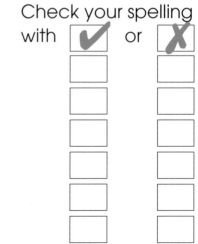

When adding -**ing** to a word ending in 'silent e', **drop** the letter **e** before adding -**ing**.

make - making

Cross off the letter **e** and add -**ing** to these words:

make		care		like	
bake		dare		hike	
hide		wipe		love	
ride		bite		move	

When adding -**ing** to a word ending in a consonant with a vowel before it, **double** the consonant before adding -ing.

ru**n** - ru**nn**ing

Draw a line to join these words correctly:

hop	shopping	clap	slipping	drip	tapping
stop	dropping	spin	clapping	tap	tipping
shop	hopping	run	spinning	skip	dripping
drop	stopping	slip	running	tip	skipping

Read the clues.   Write the answers in the crosswords.

1 down
We wear these
on our fingers.

1 across
A bird uses these
to fly.

2 down
A wasp can do
this.

2 across
To move to and fro.

3 down
These men wear
crowns.

3 across
A blackbird
does this.

4 down
To hold on
tightly.

4 across
To fetch and carry.

Comprehension

Read about **The Giant Pwanku**.

The Chinese have a story which tells how the first man hatched from an egg. This man grew two metres taller every day and became the giant Pwanku. With his pet tortoise for company, Pwanku pushed the sky up above the earth and carved the mountains and valleys with his great chisel. The sweat that poured from his body became rain. When he died his left eye became the sun and his right eye became the moon. His voice stayed behind to echo through the mountains as thunder.

Read the questions.

Put a tick by the correct answer.

Pwanku's pet was a . . . ?

1

2   Each day Pwanku grew . . . ?

2 metres ☐   2 centimetres ☐   2 miles ☐

3   The sweat from Pwanku's body became . . . ?

snow ☐   hail ☐   rain ☐

Read each question.

Write the answer on the line.

1   What did Pwanku carve with his chisel?

2   What happened to his left eye when he died?

3   What did his voice sound like when it echoed through the mountains?

Draw a ring round the best set of words for your answer.

1   The word **giant** means . . .

of great
size

very
beautiful

rather
foolish

2   The word **echo** means . . .

a sound that
crackles

a sound which
bounces back

a gurgling
sound

3   The word **carved** means . . .

cut into
shapes

a kind of
shelter

hidden
away

Write this sentence in your best handwriting:

This story about the first man comes from China.

9

Which is it?

Some pairs of words sound alike but have different meanings and spellings.

A **pear** is a fruit.

A **pair** is two of something.

Read these pairs of words:

I and eye   not and knot   be and bee   son and sun

to and two   meet and meat   tale and tail   flour and flower

Write the correct word from the box in each space.

1 | not / knot | I tied a [   ] in my shoe lace.

2 | sun / son | The [   ] was hidden behind the clouds.

3 | to / two | I have [   ] be home by [   ] o'clock.

4 | meet / meat | [   ] me at the Post Office.

5 | flour / flower | [   ] is used to make cakes.

6 | bee / be | A buzzing [   ] flew into the garden.

7 | tale / tail | The story was a [   ] of a dragon with a huge [   ].

8 | eye / I | [   ] have a fly in my [   ].

There means . . . in that place.

I live over **there**.

Their means . . . belonging to them.
They played with **their** toys.

Complete these sentences with **there** or **their**.

1   Tom and Ann went to visit [   ] grandparents.

2   [   ] grandfather met them at the station.

3   He waited [   ] until the children arrived.

4   Then they all walked to [   ] house.

5   They had never been [   ] before.

6   [   ] were lots of stairs up to [   ] grandparents' house.

7   The children showed off [   ] school reports.

8   Tom and Ann enjoyed [   ] visit and wanted to go [   ] again.

Read the labels and spot the mistakes.

By our ripe pears

By . . . means near.

That's better! Buy . . . means to get something by paying for it.

Buy our ripe pears

Write the correct labels.

Ripe pears By now

Best grapefruit To four the price of one

Fresh flours Lovely cent

Eat meet every weak

Punctuation

A sentence must begin with a **capital** letter and end with a **full stop**.
A sentence must also have a **verb** and make **sense**.

This is a complete sentence:

Two kites flew in the sky.

This is **not** a complete sentence:

kites in the sky

Which is the complete sentence?

Write the complete sentence on the lines.

1   The children ran across the field.
    Children across the field.

2   in a large garden the house
    The house stood in a large garden.

3   The rabbit into its burrow
    The rabbit hopped into its burrow.

4   The angry bull chased the boy.
    The boy and the angry bull.

There are five sentences in this paragraph. Read it aloud to yourself.

early one morning our cat walked down the garden path next it crept quietly across the grass at that moment a young blue-tit flew out of its nest in the yew tree i opened the window and clapped my hands the blue-tit flew back to its nest.

Write the paragraph in sentences with capital letters and full stops.

This is a
question mark: ?

A sentence which asks a question
ends with a question mark.

Do you know
the way to the
Post Office?

What's
your
name?

Where did
you put
your shoes?

Write a question in each balloon for the pictures.

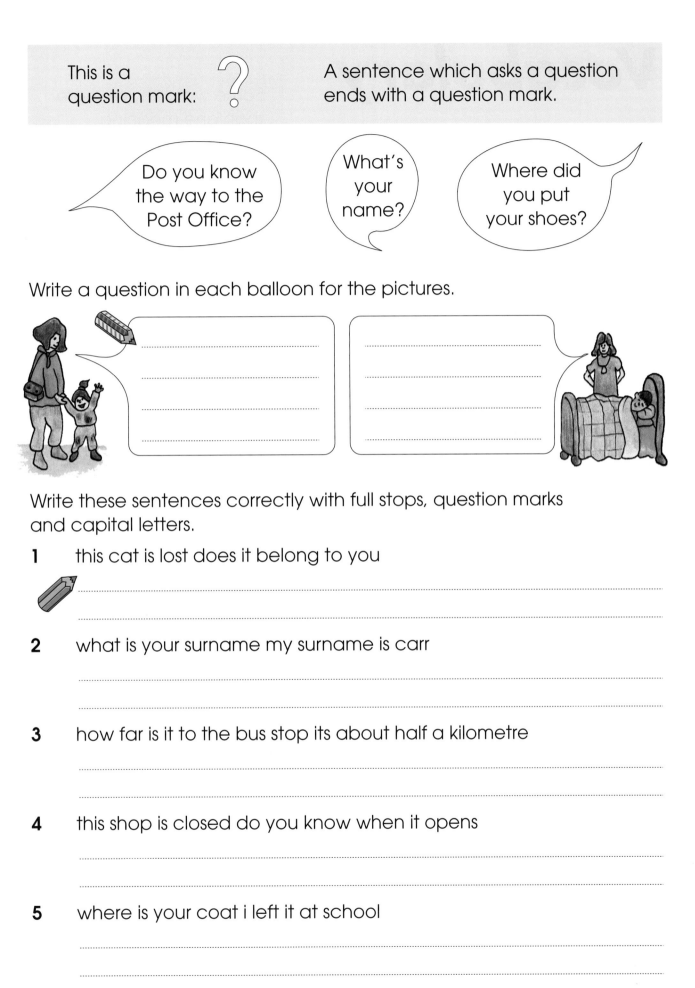

Write these sentences correctly with full stops, question marks
and capital letters.

1   this cat is lost does it belong to you

2   what is your surname my surname is carr

3   how far is it to the bus stop its about half a kilometre

4   this shop is closed do you know when it opens

5   where is your coat i left it at school

Vocabulary

Some words have **more** than one meaning.

The clue to the missing word in the balloons is in the meaning of the whole sentence.

There is a .... on the window pane.

I would like to .... my kite in the park

Do you think the missing word is:
balloon
bee
fly

Write your answer here:

Write the **same** missing word in each pair of balloons.

1
When John used his cricket .... the handle broke.

There is a .... flying high up in the barn.

2
The gate .... is falling down.

I am going to .... this letter.

3
I enjoyed acting in our school ....

The two boys went out to .... with their friends.

Read these word meanings:

and stamp . . . 'to bring your foot down heavily'

stamp

and swallow . . . 'to let food go down your throat'

swallow

and light . . . 'having very little weight'

light

and train . . . 'to get ready by practising'

train

Write the correct word in each pair of sentences.

1 Put a [ ] on the letter.
Don't [ ] your foot again.

2 A [ ] has a forked tail.
[ ] this medicine quickly.

3 A feather is [ ] in weight.
The sun gives a bright [ ].

4 The [ ] left the station.
I shall [ ] hard to get fit.

14

Step words   All the words on the steps begin with **hand**.

H	A	N	D				
H	A	N	D	Y			
H	A	N	D	L	E		
H	A	N	D	B	A	G	
H	A	N	D	S	O	M	E

Complete the step words by writing **one** letter in each empty space. Your dictionary will help you.

s	e	a				

something to sit on

s	e	a				

these animals live in the sea

s	e	a				

to look for something

s	e	a				

plants which grow in the sea

s	e	a				

c	a	n				

a kind of stick

c	a	n				

a light, narrow boat

c	a	n				

a yellow song bird

c	a	n				

sticks of wax used as lights

c	a	n				

Complete these sentences by writing the missing letters in the unfinished words.

1   This bus will _ _ _ _ t thirty people.

2   The door _ _ _ _ _ l e came off in my hand.

3   The pirates began to _ _ _ _ r c h for hidden treasure.

4   The woman paddled down river in her _ _ _ o e .

5   A _ _ _ _ _ s o m e prince came riding up to the palace.

6   The _ _ _ _ a r y sang a tuneful song.

Spelling

 Some **pairs** of vowels go together to make **one** sound.

Write **ee** in the words on the tree. Write **oo** in the words in the boot.

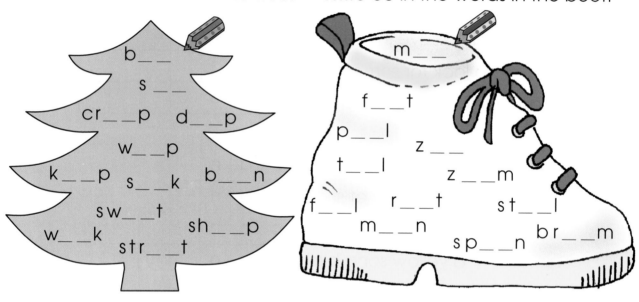

b_ _ _

s _ _ _

cr_ _ _p   d_ _ _p

w_ _ _p

k_ _ _p   s_ _ _k   b_ _ _n

sw_ _ _t

w_ _ _k   sh_ _ _p

str_ _ _t

m_ _ _

f_ _ _t

p_ _ _l   z_ _ _

t_ _ _l   z_ _ _m

f_ _ _l   r_ _ _t   st_ _ _l

m_ _ _n

sp_ _ _n   br_ _ _m

Write an **ee** word or an **oo** word to complete each sentence.

1   Wild animals can be kept in a _____ .

2   There are seven days in a _____ .

3   The _____ comes out at night.

4   To _____ is to move quietly.

5   Another word for cry is _____ .

6   A baby _____ is called a lamb.

7   The _____ of a plant grows underground.

8   A _____ is a tool for sweeping.

Write **oa** or **ai** in these words:

r _ _ s t   p _ _ n   f l _ _ t   p _ _ n t

r _ _ n   b _ _ t   d r _ _ n   b _ _ s t

Write an **oa** or **ai** word to complete each sentence.

1   Corks [   ] on water.

2   [   ] is used to colour things.

3   To [   ] is to cook in an oven or over a fire.

4   [   ] falls in drops from the sky.

5   To [   ] is to praise yourself.

6   To [   ] is to empty liquid out of something.

7   [   ] is an unpleasant feeling in the body.

8   A [   ] is a ship of any size.

Use **LOOK SAY COVER WRITE CHECK** to learn how to spell these words:

moon	
broom	
three	
sheep	
boat	
goat	
train	
chair	

Which is it?

Complete these sentences using **was** or **were**.

1   All three cups [____] broken.   2   One cup [____] broken.

3   The honey [____] sweet.   4   The rabbits [____] hungry.

5   The wind [____] cold and snowflakes [____] falling.

6   We [____] pleased because it [____] a sunny day.

7   When my presents [____] opened I [____] very happy.

8   It [____] 4 o'clock, so we [____] all going home.

Use **has** for **one** person or thing **except** with I or you.

Use **have** for **more than one**.

Write either **has** or **have** in each space.

1   A giraffe [____] a long neck.

2   Giraffes [____] long legs and long necks.

3   Our dog [____] three new puppies.

4   What [____] we got for supper today?

5   I [____] a ticket for the match tomorrow.

6   [____] you forgotten your dinner money again?

7   The boy [____] a bat and the girls [____] two balls.

8   Tom [____] eaten one cake, but his sisters [____] eaten two.

Singular means **one** of anything.

a flower

Plural means **more than one**.

a bunch of flower**s**

The letter **s** is usually added to the noun when there is more than one.

Write the following phrases with the correct word from the brackets.

1   a choir of (singer   singers)

2   an old (house   houses)

3   an orchard of (tree   trees)

4   a swarm of (bee   bees)

5   a bunch of (grape   grapes)

6   a shiny, red (apple   apples)

Some **unusual** plurals.	
singular	**plural**
1 loaf	loaves
2 leaf	leaves
3 wife	wives

	singular	**plural**
4	knife	knives
5	lady	ladies
6	cherry	cherries
7	fly	flies
8	cry	cries

Write the answers in the puzzle.

1   the singular of leaves

2   the singular of loaves

3   the plural of fly

4   the plural of wife

5   the plural of lady

6   the singular of cherries

Comprehension

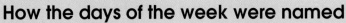

How the days of the week were named

Sunday, the first day of the week, was named after the god of the sun.

The Anglo-Saxons named Monday after the goddess of the moon. They named Tuesday in honour of another god, Tiw, who had fought a battle with a fierce wolf. Wednesday was once Wodensday. Woden was their god of war. Thor was the powerful thunder god. When he was angry he rode his chariot across the sky and threw thunderbolts and lightning at anyone who upset him. His name has become our Thursday.

Frig was the goddess of spring. Her name became Friday. Saturday is Saturn's day, named after Saturn who ruled the world with his great scythe.

Read the questions.

Put a tick under the correct answer.

1   Which is the first day of the week?

Saturday	Monday	Sunday
☐	☐	☐

2   Who is Monday named after?

the goddess of the moon	the goddess of spring	the god of war
☐	☐	☐

3   What weapon did Saturn have?

a spear	a sword	a scythe
☐	☐	☐

Read each question about the god Thor.
Write the answers on the line.

1   How did Thor ride across the sky?

2   What did he throw when he was
     angry?

3   Why did he do this?

Draw a ring round the best set of words.

1   The word **powerful** means . . .

     rather   having great   crushed
     strange   strength   into dust

2   The word **battle** means . . .

     a servant in   a container   a fight between
     a big house   for liquids   two sides

Answer these questions in sentences.

1   Why did the Anglo-Saxons
     honour Tiw?

2   How was Tiw honoured?

Write the days of the week in your best handwriting, beginning
with Sunday.

Spelling

The two letters **p** > **h** can be pushed together **p** > **h** to sound like the (f) sound as in **fox**.

Write **ph** to complete each word.

ele __ __ ant

__ __ otogra __ __

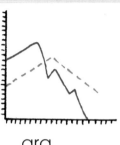

gra __ __

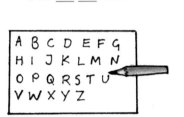

al __ __ abet

tele __ __ one

dol __ __ in

These sets of letters are sometimes found at the beginning of words:

    spr-   **shr-**
    spl-   **squ-**

Complete these verbs by writing **spr-**, **spl-**, **shr-**, or **squ-**.
SAY each verb as you write it.

1   To __ __ __ e a d is to lay something out flat.

2   To __ __ __ a y is to scatter in small drops.

3   To __ __ __ i r t is to send out a jet of liquid.

4   To __ __ __ e e z e is to press something from opposite sides.

5   To __ __ __ i e k is to scream.

6   To __ __ __ e d is to cut or tear into thin strips.

7   To __ __ __ i t is to divide or cut something.

8   To __ __ __ u t t e r is to make spitting sounds.

Some letters are written in words but make **no** sound.

<u>w</u>rite   <u>k</u>nee   clim<u>b</u>

Draw a ring round the **silent letter** of each word.

comb	lamb	wriggle	wrap
write	knight	knock	knot
knife	wrong	wrist	climb
crumb	kneel	thumb	

Write the words in three sets.

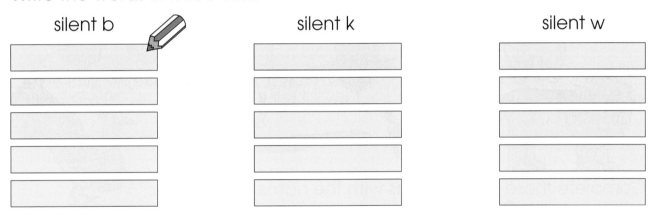

silent b   silent k   silent w

The letters in each outline have been jumbled up.

Write the correct spelling for each one.

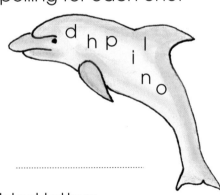

Try unscrambling these jumbled letters.

n e k e l   r i t e w   t b h u m

....

k o n w   r i w t s   m u b r c

....

Comparisons

When you **compare** two things, you say what is the **same** or what is **alike** about them.

Quiet means 'without a sound'.

'as quiet as a mouse'

Animal names can make word pictures to show how two things are alike in some way.

Complete these **comparisons** with the names of animals:

1   as wise as an

2   as brave as a

3   as proud as a

4   as busy as a

5   as weak as a

6   as slippery as an

7   as stubborn as a

8   as cunning as a

Draw a ring round the word in the brackets which makes the best **comparison**.

1   as flat as a (house, pancake, bungalow)

2   as quick as (lightning, snow, hail)

3   as deaf as a (eye, post, ear)

4   as smooth as (velvet, cotton, lace)

5   as warm as (cheese, butter, toast)

6   as dry as (hungry, thirsty, dust)

Compare the **size** of the two snakes.

Compare the **sizes** and answer the questions.

1   Which is smaller, a goldfish or a whale?

2   Which is taller, a bungalow or a castle?

3   Which is bigger, an ant or an elephant?

4   Which is higher, a flowerpot or a tower?

5   Which is shorter, a centimetre or a metre?

Stegosaurus   Tyrannosaurus   Apatosaurus

Complete these **comparisons**.

	one	**of two**	**of three**
1	slow	slower	slowest
2	fast	faster	
3	old		oldest
4		younger	youngest
5		harder	
6		softer	

Grammar

Remember! I'm **E**llie the **e**lephant.

Ordinary nouns are called **common nouns** and begin with a small letter. **Proper nouns** begin with a capital letter.

Draw a ring around the **common nouns** in this list.

july	toy	balloon
ruler	england	house
mary	chair	friday
pen	paris	william

Write the **proper nouns**, with capital letters, here:

Remember! I belong to a **herd**.

A **collective noun** names a group of people or things.

Add the missing letter for each word to make a **collective noun**.

a _lock of sheep

a _rew of sailors

a flee_ of ships

a _lass of children

an arm_ of soldiers

a _ibrary of books

Remember! I **eat** leaves.

A **verb** tells us what is being done in a sentence.

Write a sentence of your own using each of these **verbs**:

eating   sleeping   playing

1 ....

2 ....

3 ....

Remember! I have a **long** trunk.

An **adjective** describes a noun.

Write an **adjective** of your choice in each space.

1 The _____ elephant trampled over the _____ grass.

2 A _____ man was carrying a _____ sack.

3 The Queen wore a _____ crown and a _____ jewel.

4 _____ children were flying their _____ kites.

5 A _____ eagle swooped down on the _____ rabbit.

I come from India. I am an **Indian** elephant.

Adjectives can be made from the names of countries.
country — India   adjective — Indian

Join the name of the **country** to the correct **adjective**.

Africa   Russian   England   Irish

America   African   Ireland   Danish

Russia   American   Denmark   English

Write the first letter of each picture underneath.

....

Write the word you have made here.

 ....

English usage

who	**which**
Use the word **who** for **people**.	Use the word **which** for **things**.

Write these sentences using the correct ending.

1   A person ⟨ who sings is a singer.
               which sings is a singer.

2   I picked up the pen ⟨ who was on the table.
                          which was on the table.

3   We got on the train ⟨ who was in the station.
                           which was in the station.

4   Jenny was the one ⟨ who won the prize.
                        which won the prize.

Read the sentence aloud. Listen for the correct word.
Write the correct sentence.

1   Janet ⎡ did ⎤ her work.
          ⎣ done ⎦

4   The oven ⎡ is ⎤ very hot.
             ⎣ his ⎦

2   I have ⎡ did ⎤ my homework.
           ⎣ done ⎦

5   He was ⎡ as ⎤ white ⎡ as ⎤ a ghost.
          ⎣ has ⎦   ⎣ has ⎦

3   Mr Sims lost ⎡ is ⎤ hat.
                 ⎣ his ⎦

6   Ahmet ⎡ as ⎤ brown eyes.
          ⎣ has ⎦

The meaning of a sentence can be completely changed by adding **no** or **not**.

Read these sentences.

Write each sentence adding **no** or **not** to make it mean the opposite.

1   This is true.

2   My dog is friendly.

3   Reading is difficult.

4   I have money.

5   Bananas do grow here.

Write these joined words as **two** separate words using **not**.

1   don't   do not

2   can't

3   isn't

4   wouldn't

5   didn't

6   aren't

Write **one** of these words in each sentence.

nothing	nobody
nowhere	none

1   The homeless man had   to go.

2   I said   about the paint on the carpet.

3   My sister wanted some money but I had   .

4   ever went to see the lonely old lady.

Vocabulary

a nice person
a nice drink
a nice holiday
a nice cake
a nice film
a nice book

What's nice?

Some more interesting adjectives
to describe things that are nice are:

pleasant   enjoyable   good
friendly   kind   likeable
tasty   delicious   fine

Write an **interesting** adjective to describe:

a [   ] drink   a [   ] book   a [   ] holiday

a [   ] cake   a [   ] film   a [   ] person

What's nasty?
Some more interesting adjectives
to describe things that are nasty are:

awful   distasteful   bitter
terrible   horrible   upsetting
shocking   ghastly   horrific

Write an **interesting** adjective to describe:

a [   ] taste   a [   ] smell   a [   ] sight

a [   ] sound   a [   ] touch   a [   ] feeling

What's super?
Some more interesting adjectives
to describe things that are super are:

brilliant   wonderful
dazzling   magnificent
glorious   impressive   superb

Write an **interesting** adjective to describe:

a [   ] party   a [   ] dancer   a [   ] view

a [   ] present   a [   ] sportsman   a [   ] programme

Make a **word chain** of interesting words to describe:

a monster

a flower garden

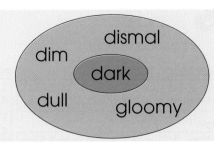

Similar means of the **same** sort.

All these words have **similar** meanings.

dismal
dim
dark
dull
gloomy

Write **two** more words having a similar meaning for:

huge

clever

happy

dirty

sad

ugly

Write each sentence giving a word of **similar** meaning to the one underlined.

1 Everything in the <u>dark</u> forest was quiet.

....

2 A <u>huge</u> wave crashed against the rocks.

....

3 All the <u>dirty</u> clothes were put in the washing machine.

....

Opposite means one of two things which are **completely different**.

Join the words which are **opposite** in meaning.

wise	strong	fit	unwell	friendly	unable
rough	foolish	well	untidy	able	unfriendly
sour	smooth	tidy	untie	kind	uncover
weak	sweet	tie	unfit	cover	unkind

Write each sentence giving an **opposite** meaning to the underlined words.

1 I am <u>unable</u> to <u>untie</u> this knot.

....

2 Those children are <u>unfriendly</u> and <u>unkind</u>.

....

Answers

page 2

h d r, Z K V, l o s w, J N R V, C f l M

bird	England	bunch
fish	Ireland	fleet
insect	Scotland	pack
reptile	Wales	tribe

cry, roar, shout, yell
chat, laugh, smile, talk
jog, run, skip, trot

page 3

table, telescope, tiger, torch
ball, bird, book, bus
same, several, single, solid, sure
bare, beyond, bitter, boast, burn

page 4

1 a soft cushion   6 a round circle
2 a sharp knife   7 a tasty sausage
3 an empty cup   8 a stormy sea
4 a high mountain   9 a brave soldier
5 an ugly monster   10 a happy face

page 5

1 green 2 yellow 3 red   4 blue
5 silver, gold   6 yellow, white, red etc.

2 four	fourth
3 six	sixth
4 nine	ninth
5 eleven	eleventh
6 twelve	twelfth

1 red, white and blue
2 third 3 first   4 five
5 red and blue or green and pink etc.

page 7

making, baking, hiding, riding
caring, daring, wiping, biting
liking, hiking, loving, moving

hop	hopping	clap	clapping
stop	stopping	spin	spinning
shop	shopping	run	running
drop	dropping	slip	slipping

drip	dripping
tap	tapping
skip	skipping
tip	tipping

1 down: rings   **3 down:** kings
1 across: wings   **3 across:** sings
2 down: sting   **4 down:** cling
2 across: swing   **4 across:** bring

page 8

1 tortoise   2 2 metres   3 rain

page 9

1 mountains and valleys
2 It became the sun.
3 thunder

1 of great size
2 a sound which bounces back
3 cut into shapes

page 10

1 knot   2 sun   3 to, two   4 Meet
5 Flour 6 bee   7 tale, tail 8 I, eye

page 11

1 their 2 Their 3 there 4 their 5 there
6 There, their   7 their   8 their, there

Ripe pears	Best grapefruit
Buy now	Two for the price of one
Fresh flowers	Eat meat
Lovely scent	every week

page 12

1 The children ran across the field.
2 The house stood in a large garden.
3 The rabbit hopped into its burrow.
4 The angry bull chased the boy.

Early one morning…
Next it crept quietly…
At that moment…
I opened the…
The blue-tit…

page 13

For example: Why are your clothes dirty?
                    How are you feeling?

1 This cat is lost. Does it belong to you?
2 What is your surname? My surname is Carr.
3 How far is it to the bus stop? It's about half a kilometre.
4 This shop is closed. Do you know when it opens?
5 Where is your coat? I left it at school.

page 14

fly   1 bat   2 post   3 play
1 stamp, stamp   3 light, light
2 swallow, Swallow   4 train, train

page 15

seat, seals, search, seaweed

cane, canoe, canary, candles

1 seat   2 handle   3 search
4 canoe 5 handsome   6 canary

page 16

1 zoo   2 week 3 moon 4 creep
5 weep 6 sheep 7 root 8 broom

page 17

| roast | pain | float | paint |
| rain | boat | drain | boast |

1 float 2 Paint 3 roast 4 Rain
5 boast 6 drain 7 Pain 8 boat

page 18

1 were 2 was   3 was   4 were
5 was, were   6 were, was
7 were, was   8 was, were

1 has   2 have 3 has   4 have
5 have 6 Have 7 has, have
8 has, have

page 19

1 singers   2 house   3 trees
4 bees   5 grapes 6 apple
1 leaf   2 loaf   3 flies
4 wives   5 ladies 6 cherry

page 20

1 Sunday   2 the goddess of the moon
3 a scythe

page 21

1 in his chariot
2 thunderbolts and lightning
3 For example: Because people sometimes upset him and made him angry.

1 having great strength
2 a fight between two sides

1 For example: Because he had fought a battle with a fierce wolf.
2 For example: They named Tuesday after him.

Sunday, Monday, Tuesday,
Wednesday, Thursday, Friday, Saturday

page 22

1 spread 2 spray 3 squirt 4 squeeze
5 shriek 6 shred 7 split 8 splutter

page 23

comb, lamb, climb, crumb, thumb
knight, knock, knot, knife, kneel
wriggle, wrap, write, wrong, wrist

elephant	dolphin	telephone
kneel	write	thumb
know	wrist	crumb

page 24

1 owl   2 lion   3 peacock 4 bee
5 kitten 6 eel   7 mule   8 fox
1 pancake 2 lightning 3 post
4 velvet 5 toast   6 dust

page 25

1 a goldfish 2 a castle   3 an elephant
4 a tower   5 a centimetre
2 fastest   3 older   4 young
5 hard, hardest   6 soft, softest

page 26

common nouns: toy, balloon, ruler, house, chair, pen
proper nouns: July, England, Mary, Friday, Paris, William

flock, crew, fleet, class, army, library

page 27

Africa	African	England	English
America	American	Ireland	Irish
Russia	Russian	Denmark	Danish

adjective